Mary Had a Little Lamb

Illustrated by Pat Nessling

ISBN-0-8136-3312-5   1 2 3 4 5   87 86 85

Mary had a little lamb,
    Its fleece was white as snow,

And everywhere that Mary went,
The lamb was sure to go.

It followed her to school one day,
Which was against the rule.

It made the children laugh and play,
To see a lamb in school.

9

And so the teacher turned it out,
But still it lingered near,

And waited patiently about
Till Mary did appear.

13

Mary had a little lamb,
   Its fleece was white as snow,
And everywhere that Mary went,
   The lamb was sure to go.

It followed her to school one day,
   Which was against the rule.
It made the children laugh and play,
   To see a lamb in school.

14

And so the teacher turned it out,
  But still it lingered near,
And waited patiently about
  Till Mary did appear.

Why does the lamb love Mary so?
  The eager children cry.
Why, Mary loves the lamb, you
  know,
  The teacher did reply.

16